Morgan Manages Her Money

www.srdharrisbooks.com

Published by S.R.D. Harris Books, LLC. Proudly printed in the USA.
Written by: S.R.D. Harris   Illustrated by: Barry Davian

Morgan has a big problem
and this is what it is...

She always spends her money,
shopping with her friend Liz.

I know I should save my money
for a rainy day.
But, when it rains outside,
we just stay inside and play.

I look up to my big sister Maya.
She always knows what to do!

She saves and spends her money,
and works for her goals, too.

I fall asleep wondering,
why can't everything be free?

Or maybe something even better...
why doesn't money grow on trees?

Next thing I know,
I am walking in the dark.
When right there in front of me,
an owl appears on the tree bark.

The wise owl was
teaching his forest friends,
all the reasons why
it's not wise to only spend.

The kind owl invites me
on a journey to see,
how to spend and
save money responsibly.

Wants | Needs

"Understanding the difference
between your wants and needs,

**will help you to grow
your valuable money seeds."**

"Wisely saving and
investing will give you
more in the end.
As long as you save, give,
and not only spend!"

"Yes, but there is so much cool stuff that I want to buy! Being wise is hard. I don't know why."

"Take a look around
at my forest friends."

"They can show you how
we save, give and spend."

Morgan wakes up and writes down
her new money plan.
She will spend less, give more
and save all that she can!

These lessons Morgan will carry
all throughout her life!

She will forever be grateful
for her dream
with Owl that night!

My Money Plan

Name _____

SAVE

GIVE

SPEND

srdharrisbooks.com

My Saving Plan

Name _____

WAYS TO EARN

I AM SAVING FOR

srdharrisbooks.com

Note to Readers:

It is never too early to teach healthy money habits to children! Morgan's mission is to spark age-appropriate conversations around spending vs. saving, delayed gratification and giving to others.

We hope you use this book as a tool to teach children how to handle money responsibly and build a strong foundation of financial literacy that will last a lifetime!

Dedication:

This book is dedicated to my amazing husband and our three wonderful daughters! Thank you for your constant support, love, and encouragement!

Special thanks to my Co-Author Camryn who helps me with all of my books and to Morgan who inspired this book!

To readers all over the globe-remember to save, give, and spend money responsibly! To our wonderful friends and family, thank you for your continued support!

In loving memory of my first hero and best friend, my Daddy, T. E. Harris.

Visit srdharrisbooks.com to learn about all of our uplifting books! Please sure to like, share and REVIEW our books!

srdharrisbooks.com

Printed in the USA
CPSIA information can be obtained
at www.ICGtesting.com
LVHW061409261023
761973LV00007B/146